W9-AKC-247

HOUGHTON MIFFLIN

Reading

We Can
Do It!

HOUGHTON MIFFLIN

BOSTON

Printed in China

ISBN-13: 978-0-618-16206-2

ISBN-10: 0-618-16206-2

14-SDP-08 07

Design, Art Management, and Page Production: Studio Goodwin Sturges

Contents

Sport Gets a Bath

by Pat Brennan
illustrated by Diane Palmisciano

"Good morning, Kim," said Norm. "What's under the porch? I hear snoring!"

"It's my dog, Sport!" sighed Kim. "She is sleeping on the ground."

"Sport's coat is full of muck!"
said Kim. "She needs a bath now."
"That's a big chore, but we can
do it," said Norm.

"Squeeze Sport tightly,
Norm. I'll use the hose," said
Kim. "Sport will have no more
muck!"

"Help!" yelled Norm. "You got me. Sport is dry, but my top is wet!"

"Oops!" said Kim. "The hose spun around."

"Look at Sport now. Her coat isn't black at all. Sport's coat is yellow!" said Norm.

"No, Sport!" shouted Kim.
"Don't shake! My top is
soaked!"

"Look, Mom," cried Kim. "We gave Sport a bath. Not much is on her coat."

"Sport looks good," said Mom, "but who is more wet? Is it Sport or you and Norm?"

Home Run

by Patrick Bracken
illustrated by Paul Meisel

"Can you play this morning,
Sam?" asked Kirk.

"Yes," said Sam. "I'll bring
Jane, too. I will teach her a
new sport."

The kids began to play. Kirk's team scored three runs. Sam's team scored three runs, too. The game was tied.

It was Jane's turn at bat. Her
team needed one more run.
Everyone knew Jane could not
score.

Jane got a big hit! She ran to
first base. Kirk threw to get her
out. He threw too high! It went
over a boy's head at first base.

Jane ran to second base.
Again, Kirk's team threw. This
time it went over a girl at second
base. Jane ran to third base!

Sam yelled, "Stay at third base."

The team shouted, "Run home, Jane. Run home!"

18

Jane tore off.

"She's going home, just like you said!" smiled Sam. "That's really a home run!"

Pet Store

by Eileen McGaferty
illustrated by Renée Andriani

"Look, Dad!" cried Jake. "It's a pet store. Can we go inside?"

"Why not?" smiled Dad. "We can make one more stop before we go home."

Inside, Jake saw lots of
tanks and cages with all sorts
of pets in them. Jake did not
know where to turn first!

The first pet Jake saw was a
big blue bird on a perch. This
bird made Jake laugh. It didn't
chirp. It squawked, "Good morning!"

23

The second pet Jake saw was a green and yellow bird with spots on its head. This bird used its beak to break open nuts.

Then Jake saw a cat with
soft gray fur. It purred when it
saw Jake and Dad.

Just then, the store clerk
came by.

"There is one more thing
you must see!" she said.

"These pups were born this morning," said the clerk. She pointed out five sleeping pups curled up by their mom.

"Wow!" Jake shouted. "This is the best thing I've seen all week!"

Big Star's Gifts

by Pat Brennan
illustrated by Marlene McDonald

Barb woke up. She got out
of bed and looked outside.
Her whole yard was snowy!

Barb got dressed quickly.
Then she ran to the back yard.
She picked a place to make her
snowman. Then she got started.
She worked hard all morning.

Barb's hard work paid off.
Her piles of snow started to look
like a real snowman. The hard
part of her job was done.

Now came the fun part. Barb made a face out of big dark prunes. She used sharp sticks to make arms.

Barb tied a red scarf on the snowman's neck. She placed a cap on his head. Then she gave the snowman a name. She named him Big Star.

For days, Big Star stood
smiling in Barb's yard. Then one
day he melted. But he left gifts
in Barb's yard.

34

Here is what Big Star left for Barb.

Car Trip

by Eileen McGaferty
illustrated by Daniel Clifford

Art's family piled in the car.
They were going to Gram's
farm. It was far. Dad started to
drive.

Dad stopped at a pay booth. He stretched out his arm and threw in coins.

"Are we at Gram's yet?" asked Art.

"We've hardly started," Meg laughed.

As Dad drove, Meg and Art saw lots of farms and barns.

"Are we at Gram's yet?" asked Art.

Dad stopped at a park to eat, rest, and play. Art ran and ran. At last Meg caught him. Then it was back in the car.

The sun started to set. Soon
it was dark. Meg and Art saw
stars above them in the night
sky. Art leaned on Meg.

"Are we at Gram's yet?"
he asked.

Meg had an idea.

"I will tell you clues," said Meg. "You name the animal on the card."

They played and played.

Then Mom yelled, "We are
at Gram's now!"

"Already?" asked Art.

And Mom, Dad, and Meg
laughed hard.

Mark's Part

by Pat Brennan
illustrated by John Nez

"Mom, Mom!" shouted Mark.
"I got a part in the class play!"

Mark showed Mom his dark
cape. He would wear it when
he marched on stage.

"Mom, how will you know me?" he asked. "Five other kids have dark capes, too."

Mom said, "I am smart enough to spot my own boy."

The next day, Mark went skating in Green Hill Park. A dog was barking at a bird and darted right into Mark. Mark fell hard against the ground.

Mark felt a sharp pain in his
arm. Soon Mark's arm was
in a cast.

At last the big day came.
Mom went to see Mark play
his part. The lights went out
and it was time to begin.

Six kids in dark capes marched on stage. Mom saw Mark right away. She waved and clapped hard. Mark felt like a star!

Ice-Cold Drinks

by Patrick Bracken
illustrated by Tricia Tusa

Rose and Bruce set up a selling
stand. Bruce wrote this:

Ice-cold drinks for sale.

Sweetest, coolest drinks in town!
Just ten cents!

Rose and Bruce waited. But
no one came for drinks.

"Maybe it needs to be
sweeter," said Bruce.

So Rose made the drinks
sweeter.

But still no one came for
drinks.

"Maybe it needs to be cooler,"
said Rose.

So Bruce made the drinks
cooler.

But still no one came for drinks.

Rose yelled, "Come and get your ice-cold drinks!"

But still no one came for
drinks.

Bruce said, "Maybe you need
to yell louder."

So Rose yelled louder.

Ice-cold drinks for sale.
Sweetest, co~~~~s in town!
~~Just ten cents~~

But still no one came for drinks.

"Maybe we need to make the price lower," said Rose.

So Bruce made the price lower.

Ice-cold drinks for
sale.
Sweetest, coolest drinks in
town!
FREE!
~~Just ten cents~~

Soon lots of people came by.
Everyone wanted the sweetest,
coolest, lowest-priced drinks
in town.

The Best Pie

by Patrick Bracken
illustrated by Rebecca Bond

Miss Cook, Miss Bake, and
Miss Sweet saw an ad. It said:
Who makes the sweetest,
lightest, moistest pie in town?
Bring your pies to the pie feast
and find out!

The three friends had the
same thoughts.

"We are each able to bake
pies," said Miss Cook. "We can
bake for the pie feast."

Miss Cook ran home. She got
her biggest bowl and started
mixing. Then she took a bite.

"It needs to be sweeter,"
she said.

Then she added sweet spices.

Miss Bake ran home. She mixed the pie filling. She took a bite.

"It needs to be lighter," she said.

Then she added an egg.

Miss Sweet ran home. She mixed and mixed, too. She took a bite.

"It needs to be moister," she said.

Then she added more milk.

At the pie feast, Sam tested
each pie. He tied a scarf over
his eyes and took a bite from
each pie.

Which pie will win?

Miss Cook, Miss Bake, and Miss Sweet each got a first-prize present—new shirts!

Don't Ask Me

by Eileen McGaferty
illustrated by Kathryn Mitter

"Happy birthday, Marge!" said
Mom. "Did Dad tell you where
we are going?"

"Not yet!" blurted Marge.

"We are going to Fred's
farm," laughed Dad.

Marge saw four new pups
at Fred's farm.

"This brown and white pup is
the runt," said Farmer Fred.
"It's the smallest. That pup
with black spots is the biggest."

"That pup with patches on its
eyes jumps highest," he added.
"This pup with white paws runs
the fastest. Which pup do you
like?"

Each pup was softer and
sweeter than the next.

"Don't ask me," sighed Marge.
"It's too hard to choose."

"Let's let a pup choose you," said Dad.

As Dad and Marge stepped back, the shortest pup jumped up. It ran after Marge, wagging its tail.

The pup wagged its tail faster and licked Marge's hand.

"I choose the pup that chose me," laughed Marge.

Now Marge has a pup named
Zoom. Zoom is the cutest,
sweetest, nicest dog around.
Just ask Marge!

Word Lists

Sport Gets a Bath (p. 5) accompanies *Two Greedy Bears.*

DECODABLE WORDS

Target Skill
r-Controlled Vowels *or, ore:*
Norm, porch, snoring, Sport, Sport's, chore

Words Using Previously Taught Skills
at, bath, big, black, but, coat, cried, dog, dry, gave, gets, got,
ground, help, hose, it's, Kim, Mom, much, muck, needs, no, oops,
shake, sighed, sleeping, soaked, spun, squeeze, that's, tightly, top,
use, wet, will, yelled, yellow

HIGH-FREQUENCY WORDS

Previously Taught
a, and, around, don't, full, good, have, hear, her, I, I'll, is, isn't,
look, looks, me, more, morning, my, now, of, on, or, said, she,
shouted, the, we, what's, who, you

Theme 10, Week 1
Home Run (p. 13) accompanies *Two Greedy Bears.*

DECODABLE WORDS

Target Skills
r-Controlled Vowels *or, ore:*
morning, sport, score, scored, tore

r-Controlled Vowels *er, ir, ur:*
Kirk, Kirk's, third

Words Using Previously Taught Skills
asked, at, base, bat, big, boy's, bring, but, can, game, get, got, high,
hit, home, it, Jane's, Jane, just, kids, knew, needed, new, ran, really,
run, runs, Sam's, Sam, smiled, stay, team, that's, this, threw, tied,
time, went, will, yelled, yes

HIGH-FREQUENCY WORDS

New
began, second

Previously Taught
a, again, could, everyone, first, girl, going, he, head, her, I, I'll, like, more, not, out, play, off, one, over, said, she's, she, shouted, teach, the, three, to, too, turn, was, you

---

Theme 10, Week 1
Pet Store (p. 21) accompanies *Two Greedy Bears.*

DECODABLE WORDS

Target Skills
r-Controlled Vowels *or, ore:*
born, sorts, store

r-Controlled Vowels *er, ir, ur:*
clerk, perch, chirp, curled, fur, purred

Words Using Previously Taught Skills
beak, best, big, cages, came, can, cat, cried, Dad, did, didn't, gray, home, it, its, it's, Jake, just, lots, made, make, mom, must, nuts, pet, pets, pointed, pups, sleeping, smiled, soft, spots, squawked, stop, tanks, them, then, these, thing, this, up, used, week, when, with, wow, yellow

HIGH-FREQUENCY WORDS

New
break, head, laugh, second

Previously Taught
a, all, and, before, bird, blue, by, first, five, go, good, green, in, inside, is, I've, know, look, more, morning, not, of, on, one, open, out, said, saw, see, seen, she, shouted, the, their, there, to, turn, was, we, were, where, why, you

Theme 10, Week 2

Big Star's Gifts (p. 29) accompanies *Fireflies for Nathan*.

DECODABLE WORDS

Target Skill
r-Controlled Vowels *ar:*
Barb, Barb's, dark, scarf, Star, Star's, yard

Words Using Previously Taught Skills
back, bed, big, but, came, cap, day, days, dressed, face, for, fun, gave, gifts, got, him, his, job, left, made, make, melted, name, named, neck, paid, picked, piles, place, placed, prunes, quickly, ran, real, red, smiling, snow, snowman, snowman's, snowy, sticks, stood, then, tied, up, used, whole, woke

HIGH-FREQUENCY WORDS

Previously Taught
a, all, and, arms, done, hard, he, head, her, here, in, is, like, look, looked, morning, now, of, off, on, one, out, outside, part, sharp, she, started, the, to, was, what, work, worked

---

Theme 10, Week 2

Car Trip (p. 37) accompanies *Fireflies for Nathan*.

DECODABLE WORDS

Target Skill
r-Controlled Vowels *ar:*
Art, Art's, barns, card, dark, farm, farms, park, stars

Words Using Previously Taught Skills
an, as, asked, at, back, booth, clues, coins, Dad, drive, drove, Gram's, had, him, his, it, last, leaned, lots, Meg, Mom, name, night, pay, piled, ran, rest, set, sky, stopped, stretched, sun, tell, them, then, threw, trip, will, yelled, yet

(Theme 10, Week 2 Car Trip continued)

HIGH-FREQUENCY WORDS

New

above, already, caught

Previously Taught

a, and, animal, are, arm, car, eat, family, far, going, hard, hardly, he, I, in, idea, laughed, now, of, on, out, play, played, said, saw, soon, started, the, they, to, was, we, were, we've, you

---

Theme 10, Week 2

Mark's Part (p. 45) accompanies *Fireflies for Nathan.*

DECODABLE WORDS

Target Skill

r-Controlled Vowels *ar:*

barking, dark, darted, marched, Mark, Mark's, Park, smart, star

Words Using Previously Taught Skills

am, asked, at, big, boy, came, cape, capes, cast, clapped, class, day, dog, fell, felt, got, ground, Hill, his, it, kids, last, Mom, next, pain, six, skating, spot, stage, time, waved, went, when, will

HIGH-FREQUENCY WORDS

New

against, begin

Previously Taught

a, and, arm, away, bird, enough, five, Green, hard, have, he, how, I, in, into, know, like, lights, me, my, on, other, out, own, part, play, right, said, saw, she, sharp, shouted, showed, soon, the, to, too, was, wear, would, you

Ice-Cold Drinks (p. 53) accompanies *The Hat*.

DECODABLE WORDS

Target Skill
Base Words and Endings -*er*, -*est:*
cooler, louder, lower, sweeter, coolest, lowest, sweetest

Words Using Previously Taught Skills
be, Bruce, but, came, cents, drinks, get, it, just, lots, made, make, maybe, need, needs, no, price, priced, Rose, sale, selling, set, stand, still, ten, this, town, up, waited, wrote, yell, yelled

HIGH-FREQUENCY WORDS

Previously Taught
a, and, by, come, everyone, for, ice-cold, in, of, one, people, said, so, soon, the, to, wanted, we, you, your

---

Theme 10, Week 3
The Best Pie (p. 61) accompanies *The Hat*.

DECODABLE WORDS

Target Skill
Base Words and Endings -*er*, -*est:*
moister, biggest, moistest, sweetest

Words Using Previously Taught Skills
ad, added, an, at, Bake, be, best, bite, bowl, bring, can, Cook, each, egg, feast, filling, from, got, had, he, his, home, it, makes, milk, Miss, mixed, mixing, needs, new, pie, pies, ran, Sam, same, scarf, shirts, spices, Sweet, tested, then, three, tied, took, town, which, will, win

HIGH-FREQUENCY WORDS

New

eyes, present, thoughts

Previously Taught

a, able, and, are, find, first-prize, for, friends, her, in, lighter, lightest, more, out, over, said, saw, she, started, the, to, too, we, who, your

---

Theme 10, Week 3
Don't Ask Me **(p. 69)** accompanies *The Hat.*

DECODABLE WORDS

Target Skill
Base Words and Endings *-er, -est:*

faster, softer, sweeter, biggest, cutest, fastest, highest, nicest, shortest, sweetest

Words Using Previously Taught Skills

added, as, ask, at, back, birthday, black, blurted, choose, chose, Dad, did, dog, each, farm, farmer, Fred, Fred's, hand, has, he, it's, it, its, just, let's, let, licked, Marge, Marge's, Mom, named, new, next, patches, paws, pup, pups, ran, runs, runt, sighed, spots, stepped, tail, tell, than, that, this, up, wagged, wagging, which, white, with, yet, Zoom

HIGH-FREQUENCY WORDS

New

eyes

Previously Taught

a, after, and, are, around, brown, do, don't, four, going, happy, hard, I, is, jumped, jumps, laughed, like, me, not, now, on, said, saw, smallest, the, to, too, was, we, where, you

81

HIGH-FREQUENCY WORDS TAUGHT TO DATE

a	buy	find	hungry	on	she	walk
able	by	first	hurt	once	shoe[s]	wall
about	call	five	I	one	shout	want
above	car	flower	idea	only	show	warm
afraid	carry	fly	in	open	sing	was
after	caught	follow	is	or	small	wash
again	children	for	jump	other	so	watched
against	climb	forest	kind	our	some	water
all	cold	found	know	out	soon	we
already	color	four	laugh[ed]	over	start	wear
also	come	friend	learn	own	sure	were
always	could	full	light	paper	table	what
and	cow	funny	like	part	talk	where
animal	dance	garden	little	people	tall	who
any	divide	girl	live	person	teacher	why
are	do	give	long	picture	the	work
arms	does	go	look	piece	their	world
around	done	goes	love	play	there	would
away	door	gone	many	present	these	write
baby	down	good	me	pretty	they	you
bear	draw	green	minute[s]	pull	thoughts	your
because	eat	grow	more	put	three	
been	edge	happy	morning	read	through	
before	eight	hard	most	ready	tiny	
began	else	have	mother	right	to	
begin[s]	enough	he	my	room	today	
bird	evening	head[s]	near	said	together	
blue	ever	hear	never	saw	too	
body	every	her	not	school	try	
both	eye[s]	here	now	second	turn	
break	fall	hold	ocean	see	two	
brown	family	horse	of	seven	under	
build	far	house	off	shall	upon	
butter	father	how	old	sharp	very	

82

Decoding skills taught to date: Consonants *m, s, t, c,* consonants *n, f, p,* short *a,* consonants *b, r, h, g,* short *i,* consonants *d, w, l, x,* short *o,* consonants *y, k, v,* short *e,* consonants *q, j, z,* short *u,* double final consonants, final consonants, plurals with *-s,* verb endings *-s, -ed, -ing,* possessives, consonant clusters with *r,* contractions with *-'s,* clusters with *l,* clusters with *s,* silent consonants *kn, wr, gn,* triple clusters, digraphs *sh, th, wh,* digraphs *ch, tch,* long *a* (CVC*e*), other consonant sounds soft *c* and *g,* final *nd, ng, nk,* long *i* (CVC*e*), contractions, long *o* (CV, CVC*e*), long *u* (CVC*e*), final *ft, lk, nt,* long *e* (CV, CVC*e*), vowel pairs *ee, ea,* vowel pairs *ai, ay,* vowel pairs *oa, ow,* sound for *oo* (as in *book*), compound words, vowel pairs *oo, ew, ue, ou,* long *i* (*igh, ie*), base words and endings *-s, -ed, -ing,* vowel pairs: other vowel sounds (*ou, ow*), syllabication, base words and endings *-ed, -ing,* sounds for *y,* base words and endings (*-es, -ies*), prefixes *un-, re-,* vowel pairs *oi, oy, aw, au,* suffixes *-ful, -ly, -y,* *r*-controlled vowels: *or, ore, r*-controlled vowels: *er, ir, ur, r*-controlled vowels: *ar,* base words and endings (*-er, -est*)